POPULAR LECTURES IN MATHEMATICS SERIES

EDITORS: I. N. SNEDDON AND M. STARK

Volume 1

THE METHOD OF MATHEMATICAL INDUCTION

TITLES IN THE POPULAR LECTURES IN MATHEMATICS SERIES

Vol. 1 *The Method of Mathematical Induction*
By I. S. SOMINSKII

Vol. 2 *Fibonacci Numbers*
By N. N. VOROB'EV

Vol. 3 *Some Applications of Mechanics to Mathematics*
By V. A. USPENSKII

Vol. 4 *Geometrical Constructions using Compasses Only*
By A. N. KOSTOVSKII

Vol. 5 *The Ruler in Geometrical Constructions*
By A. S. SMOGORZHEVSKII

Vol. 6 *Inequalities*
By P. P. KOROVKIN

THE METHOD OF
MATHEMATICAL
INDUCTION

by
I. S. SOMINSKII

Translated from the Russian by
HALINA MOSS, B.Sc.

Translation Editor
IAN N. SNEDDON
Simson Professor of Mathematics
in the University of Glasgow

BLAISDELL PUBLISHING COMPANY
NEW YORK · LONDON
A DIVISION OF RANDOM HOUSE

SOLE DISTRIBUTORS IN THE UNITED STATES AND CANADA
Blaisdell Publishing Company
22 East 51st Street, New York 22, N.Y.

A translation of the original volume
Metod matematicheskoi induktsii
(Moscow, Fizmatgiz, 1959)

Library of Congress Card Number: 61-11532

Printed in Great Britain by Pergamon Printing and Art Services Limited, London

C O N T E N T S

		Page
Foreword	. . . .	vii
INTRODUCTION	. . . .	1
CHAPTER I	The Method of Mathematical Induction . .	3
CHAPTER II	Examples and Exercises	12
CHAPTER III	The Proof by Induction of Some Theorems of Elementary Algebra	39
CHAPTER IV	Solutions	45

FOREWORD

The method of mathematical induction, which is the subject of this book, is widely applicable in all departments of mathematics, from the elementary school course up to branches of higher mathematics only lately investigated. It is clear, therefore, that even a school course of mathematics cannot be studied seriously without mastering this method. Ideas of mathematical induction, moreover, have a wide general significance and acquaintance with them also has an importance for those whose interests are far removed from mathematics and its applications.

The essentials of the method and some simple examples of its use are given in Chapter I and in the first section of Chapter II. To study these it is sufficient for the reader to be familiar with the course of mathematics in the seven year school period. The remaining sections of this book are fully accessible to the reader who has mastered the mathematics course of a full secondary school.

This book is meant for pupils in the higher forms of secondary schools, first year students in universities, teacher training colleges and technical colleges. It would also be useful for discussion in a school mathematical society.

INTRODUCTION

Propositions can be divided into general and particular. The following are examples of general propositions:

All citizens of the U.S.S.R. have the right to education.

In every parallellogram the diagonals are bisected at their point of intersection.

All numbers ending with a zero are divisible by 5.

The corresponding examples of particular propositions are as follows:

Petrov has the right to education.

In the parallellogram ABCD the diagonals are bisected at their point of intersection.

140 is divisible by 5.

The transition from general propositions to particular ones is called <u>deduction</u>. Let us consider an example:

(1) All citizens of the U.S.S.R. have the right to education.

(2) Petrov is a Soviet citizen.

(3) Petrov has the right to education.

We obtain the particular proposition (3) from the general proposition (1), with the help of the proposition (2).

Progressing from particular propositions to general ones is called <u>induction</u>. Induction can lead to correct as well as to incorrect conclusions. We shall make that clear by means of two examples:

(1) 140 is divisible by 5.

1

(2) All numbers ending in zero are divisible by 5.

From the particular proposition (1) we obtained the general proposition (2) and this proposition is correct. On the other hand:

(1) 140 is divisible by 5.

(2) All three figure numbers are divisible by 5.

From the particular proposition (1) we obtained the general proposition (2) and this proposition is wrong.

The question which then arises is how can we use induction in mathematics so as to obtain only correct conclusions? The answer to this question is given in this book.

THE METHOD OF MATHEMATICAL INDUCTION

1

First of all we examine two examples of induction which are inadmissible in mathematics.

E x a m p l e 1. Let

$$S_n = \frac{1}{1 \cdot 2} + \frac{1}{2 \cdot 3} + \frac{1}{3 \cdot 4} + \cdots + \frac{1}{n(n+1)}.$$

It is easy to verify that:

$$S_1 = \frac{1}{1 \cdot 2} = \frac{1}{2},$$
$$S_2 = \frac{1}{1 \cdot 2} + \frac{1}{2 \cdot 3} = \frac{2}{3},$$
$$S_3 = \frac{1}{1 \cdot 2} + \frac{1}{2 \cdot 3} + \frac{1}{3 \cdot 4} = \frac{3}{4},$$
$$S_4 = \frac{1}{1 \cdot 2} + \frac{1}{2 \cdot 3} + \frac{1}{3 \cdot 4} + \frac{1}{4 \cdot 5} = \frac{4}{5}.$$

On the basis of the above results we state, that for every natural n

$$S_n = \frac{n}{n+1}.$$

E x a m p l e 2. Let us examine the quadratic expression $x^2 + x + 41$, first considered by the well known mathematician Leonard Euler, one of the first of the St. Petersburg Academicians. If we substitute zero for x in this expression, we obtain the prime number 41. Again, if we substitute 1 for x in the expression, we obtain 43, which again is a prime number. Continuing to substitute successively the values 2, 3, 4, 5, 6, 7, 8, 9, 10 for x in the expression we obtain each time a prime number: 47, 53, 61, 71, 83, 97, 113, 131, 151.

3

On the basis of results obtained we state that the substitution of any positive integer for x in the above quadratic always results in a prime number.

Why is the reasoning used in these examples not acceptable in mathematics? Where is the flaw in our conclusions?

The trouble is that in both cases we made a general statement concerning any n (in the second example, any x) solely on the grounds that this proposition turned out to be true for some values of n (or x).

Induction is widely used in mathematics, but one must use it with skill. Any use of induction which is not careful might lead to false conclusions.

Thus, although in Example 1 our general proposition does in fact turn out to be true (as is proved below in Example 5), the general proposition stated in Example 2 turns out to be false.

Indeed, when the quadratic $x^2 + x + 41$ is studied more closely, it is seen that it is equal to a prime number for $x = 0, 1, 2, \ldots, 39$, but for $x = 40$ it equals 41^2, that is, it is a composite number.

2

In Example 2 we encountered a proposition valid in 40 particular cases, but still wrong in general.

We shall give two further examples of propositions which are true in several particular cases and false in general.

E x a m p l e 3. The binomial $x^n - 1$, where n is a positive integer, is of great interest to mathematicians. It is sufficient to say that it is closely connected with a geometrical problem about dividing a circumference into n equal parts.

It is not surprising, therefore, that this expression is studied extensively in mathematics. In particular, the problem of factorizing this expression into factors with integral coefficients is of great interest.

When the factors $x^n - 1$ were written out for numerous

particular values of n , it was observed that none of the coefficients was numerically larger than unity. In fact

$$x-1 = x-1,$$
$$x^2-1 = (x-1)(x+1),$$
$$x^3-1 = (x-1)(x^2+x+1),$$
$$x^4-1 = (x-1)(x+1)(x^2+1),$$
$$x^5-1 = (x-1)(x^4+x^3+x^2+x+1),$$
$$x^6-1 = (x-1)(x+1)(x^2+x+1)(x^2-x+1),$$

. . . .

Tables were compiled within which all coefficient possessed this property. Attempts to prove the property for every n failed.

In 1938, in a note in the journal <u>Uspekhi matematicheskikh nauk</u> ('Successes of Mathematical Sciences') the Soviet mathematician, N.G. Chebotarёv, challenged mathematicians to settle this question.

The solution was given by V. Ivanov*. It turned out that the above property is possessed by all polynomials of the type x^n-1 , whose degree n is less than 105. One of the factors of $x^{105}-1$, however, is the polynomial

$$x^{48}+x^{47}+x^{46}-x^{43}-x^{42}-2x^{41}-x^{40}-x^{39}+x^{36}+$$
$$+x^{35}+x^{34}+x^{33}+x^{32}+x^{31}-x^{28}-x^{26}-x^{24}-x^{22}-$$
$$-x^{20}+x^{17}+x^{16}+x^{15}+x^{14}+x^{13}+x^{12}-x^9-x^8-$$
$$-2x^7-x^6-x^5+x^2+x+1,$$

which no longer possesses this property.

E x a m p l e 4. Into how many parts is space divided by n planes all passing through one point, if no three of them pass through the same straight line?

Let us examine the simplest cases of this problem. One plane divides space into 2 parts. Two planes passing through one point divide space into 4 parts. Three planes passing through one point, but not passing through one straight line, divide space into 8 parts.

At first sight it may seem that when the number of planes is increased by 1, the number of parts into which space is divided is doubled and, thus, 4 planes will divide space

---

*V. IVANOV, <u>Usp. mat. nauk</u>, 4, 313-317 (1941).

into 16 parts, five planes into 32 parts, etc. In general n planes would split up space into 2^n parts.

In reality this does not occur: 4 planes split space up into 14 parts and 5 planes into 22 parts.

In general, n planes split space up into $n(n-1)+2$ parts.

From the examples discussed above we draw a simple but important conclusion:

A proposition can be correct for a great number of particular cases and at the same time may be false in general.

3

Now, the following question arises. We have a proposition justified in several particular cases. It is impossible to consider all particular cases. How are we to know whether the proposition is correct in general?

It is sometimes possible to answer this question by applying a special method of reasoning, called 'the method of mathematical induction' (full induction, complete induction).

At the basis of this method lies the 'principle' of mathematical induction, which may be stated in the following way:

A proposition is true for every positive integer n if:

(1) it is true for $n=1$, and

(2) it follows from the truth of the proposition for any positive integer $n=k$ that the proposition is also true for $n=k+1$.

To prove this principle let us suppose the opposite, i.e. let us suppose that the proposition is not true for every positive integer n . Then there exists a natural m , such that

(1) the proposition is not true for $n=m$,

(2) for any n smaller than m the proposition is true (in other words, m is the first integer number for which the

proposition is false).

Obviously, $m > 1$, since for $n = 1$ the proposition is true (condition 1). It follows that $m - 1$ is a positive integer. We therefore have the situation, that the proposition is true for the positive integer $m - 1$, but is false for the next integer m . This contradicts condition (2).

N o t e. While proving the principle of mathematical induction we made use of the fact that any set of positive integers contains a smallest number. It ·is easily seen that this property in its turn could be deduced as a corollary of the principle of mathematical induction. Therefore, the two propositions are equivalent. Either of them can be taken as an axiom defining the natural series; the other will then be a theorem. It is in fact usual to take the principle of induction as the axiom*.

4

A proof based on the principle of induction is called a 'proof by the method of mathematical induction' or simply, a 'proof by induction'. Such a proof must necessarily consist of proving two independent theorems.

T h e o r e m 1. The proposition is true for $n = 1$.

T h e o r e m 2. The proposition is true for $n = k + 1$ if it is true for $n = k$, where k is any positive integer.

If both these theorems are proved, then, on the basis of the principle of induction the proposition is true for any n.

E x a m p l e 5. Find the sum

$$S_n = \frac{1}{1 \cdot 2} + \frac{1}{2 \cdot 3} + \frac{1}{3 \cdot 4} + \cdots + \frac{1}{n(n+1)}.$$

(Cf. Example 1).

---

*For instance the principle of induction is the fifth axiom in Peano's scheme for the natural numbers [cf. E. Landau, 'Foundations of Analysis' (Chelsea Pub. Co., 1951), p.2] – Editor.

We know that

$$S_1 = \frac{1}{2}, \quad S_2 = \frac{2}{3}, \quad S_3 = \frac{3}{4}, \quad S_4 = \frac{4}{5}.$$

Now we shall not repeat our mistake, made in Example 1, and we shall not rush to state that for any natural n

$$S_n = \frac{n}{n+1}.$$

We shall be careful and we shall say, that the examination of S_1, S_2, S_3, S_4 allows us to put forward a hypothesis that $S_n = \frac{n}{n+1}$ for any positive integer n. We know in addition that this hypothesis is true for $n = 1, 2, 3, 4$. To test this hypothesis we shall use the method of induction.

T h e o r e m 1. <u>The hypothesis is true for</u> $n = 1$, <u>since</u> $S_1 = \frac{1}{2}$ <u>and</u> $\frac{1}{1+1} = \frac{1}{2}$.

T h e o r e m 2. <u>Let us suppose that the hypothesis</u> <u>is true for</u> $n = k$, <u>that is</u>

$$S_k = \frac{1}{1 \cdot 2} + \frac{1}{2 \cdot 3} + \cdots + \frac{1}{k(k+1)} = \frac{k}{k+1},$$

<u>where</u> k <u>is some positive integer. We shall prove that, in</u> <u>that case, the hypothesis is bound to be true also for</u> $n = k+1$, <u>that is</u>

$$S_{k+1} = \frac{k+1}{k+2}.$$

Indeed,

$$S_{k+1} = S_k + \frac{1}{(k+1)(k+2)};$$

it follows, according to the condition of the theorem, that

$$S_{k+1} = \frac{k}{k+1} + \frac{1}{(k+1)(k+2)} = \frac{k^2+2k+1}{(k+1)(k+2)} = \frac{k+1}{k+2}.$$

Both theorems are now proved. Now, on the basis of the

principle of induction we assert   that

$$S_n = \frac{n}{n+1}$$

for any positive integer n .

N o t e   1.   It is imperative to stress   that a proof by
the method of induction demands unconditionally the proof of
both Theorems 1 and 2. We have seen already that a careless
attitude to Theorem 2 is apt to lead to trouble. Now we
shall show that we must not omit to prove Theorem 1 either.
Let us look at an example to illustrate this point.

E x a m p l e   6. <u>Any natural number equals the following
natural number</u>.

We shall attempt a proof of this proposition by the method
of induction.

Let us suppose that

$$k = k + 1. \tag{1}$$

We prove that

$$k + 1 = k + 2. \tag{2}$$

Indeed, if we add 1 to each side of equation (1) we obtain
the equation (2). It emerges that if the proposition is
true for $n = k$, then it is also true for $n = k + 1$. The
theorem is thus proved.

C o r o l l a r y. <u>All natural numbers are equal</u>.

Where then is the mistake? The mistake is, that the first
theorem, necessary in the application of the principle of
mathematical induction, has not been proved and is untrue.
What has been proved was the second theorem only.

Each of Theorems 1 and 2 has its own special meaning.
Theorem 1 creates, so to speak, the basis for the carrying
out of induction. Theorem 2 gives us the right to unlimited
automatic broadening of that basis, the right of transition
from the given particular case to the following one, from
n to $n + 1$.

If Theorem 1 is not proved, and Theorem 2 is (as in Example 6), then a basis for carrying out induction has not been created and then it is absurd to apply Theorem 2 as there is nothing to broaden.

If Theorem 2 is not proved, and Theorem 1 is (as in Examples 1 and 2), then, although the basis for carrying out induction has been created, the right to broaden it is absent.

N o t e   2. The method of mathematical induction has been analysed here for the simplest case. In more complex cases the formulation of Theorems 1 and 2 should be modified correspondingly.

Sometimes the second part of a proof is based on the truth not only of the statement $n = k$ but also of $n = k+1$. In this case the statement in the first part should be tested for <u>two</u> consecutive values of n (see Problem 18 below).

Sometimes a statement is being proved not for any positive integer n, but for any integer n greater than some positive integer m. In this case, in the first part of the proof the statement is tested for $n = m+1$ and, if necessary, for several following values of n (see Problem 24 below).

5

In concluding this chapter we must return once again to Example 1, to point out an essential aspect of the method of induction.

Studying the sum

$$S_n = \frac{1}{1 \cdot 2} + \frac{1}{2 \cdot 3} + \cdots + \frac{1}{n(n+1)}$$

for different values of n , we calculated that

$$S_1 = \frac{1}{2}, \quad S_2 = \frac{2}{3}, \quad S_3 = \frac{3}{4}, \quad S_4 = \frac{4}{5}, \ldots,$$

and this led us to put forward the hypothesis that for any positive integer n

$$S_n = \frac{n}{n+1}.$$

To verify the hypothesis we employed the method of induction.

We were lucky in that we expressed a hypothesis which was confirmed. If we had been unfortunate in our choice of hypothesis then the fallacy of it would have been exposed in the course of the proof of Theorem 2.

E x a m p l e 7. We know that

$$S_n = \frac{1}{1 \cdot 2} + \frac{1}{2 \cdot 3} + \dots + \frac{1}{n(n+1)} = \frac{n}{n+1}. \tag{1}$$

Let us suppose that after studying S_n we put forward the hypothesis

$$S_n = \frac{n+1}{3n+1}. \tag{2}$$

For $n = 1$ formula (2) is correct. Let us take it that formula (2) is correct for $n = k$, i.e.

$$S_k = \frac{k+1}{3k+1},$$

and then attempt to prove that formula (2) is also correct for $n = k + 1$, i.e. that

$$S_{k+1} = \frac{k+2}{3k+4}.$$

We have

$$S_{k+1} = S_k + \frac{1}{(k+1)(k+2)} =$$
$$= \frac{k+1}{3k+1} + \frac{1}{(k+1)(k+2)} = \frac{k^3 + 4k^2 + 8k + 3}{(k+1)(k+2)(3k+1)},$$

giving a result for S_{k+1} which is different from the one we expected.

In this way it emerges that the truth of the formula (2) for $n = k + 1$ does not follow from its truth for $n = k$. We have therefore discovered that formula (2) is wrong.

In this way: <u>in the search for a general law, the method of mathematical induction allows us to test any hypotheses which are put forward, and so to discard the wrong ones, and confirm the true ones.</u>

EXAMPLES AND EXERCISES

In order to learn to use the method of induction it is necessary to discuss a sufficient number of problems.

In this chapter there are fifty-two problems. Of these twenty-two have detailed solutions in the text. The remaining thirty problems, which are intended for independent work, have solutions placed at the end of the book.

1

Problem 1. Let us write out in order of increasing magnitude the odd positive numbers 1, 3, 5, 7 ...... Let the first of them be u_1, the second u_2, the third u_3, etc., that is,

$$u_1 = 1, \qquad u_2 = 3, \qquad u_3 = 5, \qquad u_4 = 7, \ldots$$

Let us set ourselves the following task: to devise a formula for the odd number u_n, expressing it in terms of n.

S o l u t i o n.   The first odd number u_1 can be written thus:

$$u_1 = 2 \cdot 1 - 1. \tag{1}$$

The second odd number u_2 can be written thus:

$$u_2 = 2 \cdot 2 - 1. \tag{2}$$

The third odd number u_3 can be written thus:

$$u_3 = 2 \cdot 3 - 1. \tag{3}$$

If we look carefully at equations (1), (2) and (3) we are

led to the hypothesis that to obtain the nth odd number u_n it is sufficient to double its suffix n and then subtract 1; that is, for the nth odd number we have the formula

$$u_n = 2n - 1. \tag{4}$$

Let us prove that this formula is justified.

T h e o r e m 1.   Equation (1) shows that formula (4) is valid for $n = 1$.

T h e o r e m 2.   Let us suppose that the formula is valid for $n = k$, i.e. that the kth odd number is of the form:

$$u_k = 2k - 1.$$

We must now try to prove that formula (4) is bound to be valid also for the $(k+1)$th odd number, i.e. that the $(k+1)$th odd number is of the form:

$$u_{k+1} = 2(k+1) - 1,$$

or, that

$$u_{k+1} = 2k + 1.$$

To obtain the $(k+1)$th odd positive integer it is sufficient to add 2 to the kth odd integer, i.e. $u_{k+1} = u_k + 2$. Our condition is $u_k = 2k - 1$. That means that

$$u_{k+1} = (2k - 1) + 2 = 2k + 1,$$

which was what we set out to prove.

A n s w e r.   The nth odd positive integer is given by the formula

$$u_n = 2n - 1$$

Problem 2: To calculate the sum of the first n odd whole numbers. Let us call the required sum S_n , i.e.

$$S_n = 1 + 3 + 5 + \ldots + (2n - 1).$$

In mathematics there are ready-made formulae for solving such problems. We are interested in solving this problem without recourse to such a formula, but by using the method of induction.

For this we must first formulate a hypothesis, i.e. simply try and guess the answer.

We give n particular values 1, 2, 3... until we have collected enough material for the basis of a more or less reliable hypothesis. After this all that remains is to test the hypothesis by the method of mathematical induction.

We have

$$S_1 = 1, \quad S_2 = 4, \quad S_3 = 9, \quad S_4 = 16, \quad S_5 = 25, \quad S_6 = 36.$$

Now it all depends on how observant the person tackling the problem is, whether he is able to guess a general result from the particular ones.

We take it that in this case it is easy to notice that:

$$S_1 = 1^2, \quad S_2 = 2^2, \quad S_3 = 3^2, \quad S_4 = 4^2.$$

On these grounds we can suppose that in general

$$S_n = n^2.$$

We shall now prove that this hypothesis is the correct one.

T h e o r e m 1. For $n = 1$ the sum is represented by one term equal to 1. For $n = 1$ the expression n^2 also equals 1. That means that, for $n = 1$, the hypothesis is correct.

T h e o r e m 2. Let us suppose that the hypothesis is correct for $n = k$, i.e. $S_k = k^2$, and then prove that in that case the hypothesis is also correct for $n = k + 1$, i.e.

$$S_{k+1} = (k+1)^2.$$

Now

$$S_{k+1} = S_k + (2k+1).$$

and $S_k = k^2$, and therefore

$$S_{k+1} = k^2 + (2k + 1) = (k + 1)^2,$$

which was what we set out to prove.

A n s w e r.   The sum of the first n odd integers is $S_n = n^2$.

Problem 3. Find u_n, if it is known that $u_1 = 1$ and that for any natural $k > 1$

$$u_k = u_{k-1} + 3.$$

H i n t: $u_1 = 3 \cdot 1 - 2,\ u_2 = 3 \cdot 2 - 2.$

Problem 4. Find the sum

$$S_n = 1 + 2 + 2^2 + 2^3 + \ldots + 2^{n-1}.$$

H i n t: (1) $S_1 = 2 - 1;\ S_2 = 2^2 - 1;\ S_3 = 2^3 - 1;$ or

(2) examine $2S_n - S_n$.

Problem 5. Prove that the sum of the first n positive integers is equal to $\dfrac{n(n+1)}{2}$.

S o l u t i o n. This problem differs from the previous ones in that it is unnecessary to make up a hypothesis since one is already given. It is only necessary to prove that it is correct.

Let the sum required be S_n , i.e. let

$$S_n = 1 + 2 + 3 + \ldots + n.$$

T h e o r e m 1.   For $n = 1$, the hypothesis is correct.

T h e o r e m 2.   Let

$$S_k = 1 + 2 + \ldots + k = \frac{k(k+1)}{2}.$$

We shall show, that

$$S_{k+1} = \frac{(k+1)(k+2)}{2}.$$

This follows from

$$S_{k+1} = S_k + (k+1) = \frac{k(k+1)}{2} + (k+1) = \frac{(k+1)(k+2)}{2}.$$

<u>Problem 6.</u> Prove that the sum of the squares of the first n positive integers is equal to $\frac{n(n+1)(2n+1)}{6}$.

<u>Problem 7.</u> Prove that:

$$S_n = 1 - 2^2 + 3^2 - 4^2 + \ldots + (-1)^{n-1}n^2 =$$
$$= (-1)^{n-1}\frac{n(n+1)}{2}.$$

S o l u t i o n.

T h e o r e m 1. For $n=1$, the hypothesis is obviously correct since $(-1)^0 = 1$.

T h e o r e m 2. Let

$$S_k = 1 - 2^2 + 3^2 - \ldots + (-1)^{k-1}k^2 = (-1)^{k-1}\frac{k(k+1)}{2}.$$

To prove that

$$S_{k+1} = 1 - 2^2 + 3^2 - \ldots + (-1)^{k-1}k^2 + (-1)^k(k+1)^2 =$$
$$= (-1)^k\frac{(k+1)(k+2)}{2},$$

we note that

$$S_{k+1} = S_k + (-1)^k(k+1)^2 =$$
$$= (-1)^{k-1}\frac{k(k+1)}{2} + (-1)^k(k+1)^2 =$$
$$= (-1)^k\left[(k+1) - \frac{k}{2}\right](k+1) = (-1)^k\frac{(k+1)(k+2)}{2}.$$

<u>Problem 8.</u> Prove that
$$1^2 + 3^2 + 5^2 + \ldots + (2n-1)^2 = \frac{n(2n-1)(2n+1)}{3}.$$

Problem 9. Prove that the sum of the cubes of the first n positive integers is equal to $\left[\dfrac{n(n+1)}{2}\right]^2$.

Problem 10. Prove that

$$1+x+x^2+\ldots+x^n=\frac{x^{n+1}-1}{x-1}\quad(x\neq1).$$

Problem 11. Prove that

$$1\cdot2+2\cdot3+3\cdot4+\ldots+n(n+1)=\frac{n(n+1)(n+2)}{3}.$$

Problem 12. Prove that

$$1\cdot2\cdot3+2\cdot3\cdot4+3\cdot4\cdot5+\ldots+n(n+1)(n+2)=$$
$$=\frac{n(n+1)(n+2)(n+3)}{4}.$$

Problem 13. Prove that

$$\frac{1}{1\cdot3}+\frac{1}{3\cdot5}+\ldots+\frac{1}{(2n-1)(2n+1)}=\frac{n}{2n+1}.$$

Problem 14. Prove that

$$\frac{1^2}{1\cdot3}+\frac{2^2}{3\cdot5}+\ldots+\frac{n^2}{(2n-1)(2n+1)}=\frac{n(n+1)}{2(2n+1)}.$$

Problem 15. Prove that

$$\frac{1}{1\cdot4}+\frac{1}{4\cdot7}+\frac{1}{7\cdot10}+\ldots+\frac{1}{(3n-2)(3n+1)}=\frac{n}{3n+1}.$$

Problem 16. Prove that

$$\frac{1}{1\cdot5}+\frac{1}{5\cdot9}+\frac{1}{9\cdot13}+\ldots+\frac{1}{(4n-3)(4n+1)}=\frac{n}{4n+1}.$$

Problem 17. Prove that

$$\frac{1}{a(a+1)}+\frac{1}{(a+1)(a+2)}+\ldots+\frac{1}{(a+n-1)(a+n)}=$$
$$=\frac{n}{a(a+n)}.$$

<u>Problem 18</u>. Prove that, if $v_0 = 2$, $v_1 = 3$, and for any natural k

$$v_{k+1} = 3v_k - 2v_{k-1},$$

then $v_n = 2^n + 1$.

S o l u t i o n. For $n = 0$, and $n = 1$, the truth of the hypothesis is a consequence of the fact that $2^0 + 1 = 2$, $2^1 + 1 = 3$.

Let us suppose that

$$v_{k-1} = 2^{k-1} + 1; \quad v_k = 2^k + 1.$$

Then

$$v_{k+1} = 3(2^k + 1) - 2(2^{k-1} + 1) = 2^{k+1} + 1.$$

and the hypothesis is confirmed.

<u>Problem 19</u>. Prove that

$$u_n = \frac{\alpha^{n+1} - \beta^{n+1}}{\alpha - \beta},$$

if

$$u_1 = \frac{\alpha^2 - \beta^2}{\alpha - \beta}, \quad u_2 = \frac{\alpha^3 - \beta^3}{\alpha - \beta} \quad (\alpha \neq \beta),$$

and if for every integer $k > 2$

$$u_k = (\alpha + \beta) u_{k-1} - \alpha\beta u_{k-2}.$$

<u>Problem 20</u>. The product $1.2.3 \ldots n$ is denoted by $n!$ (which is read 'factorial n'). It is useful to remember that $1! = 1$, $2! = 2$, $3! = 6$, $4! = 24$, $5! = 120$.

C a l c u l a t e
$$S_n = 1 \cdot 1! + 2 \cdot 2! + 3 \cdot 3! + \ldots + n \cdot n!$$

Solution.

$$S_1 = 1 \cdot 1! = 1,$$
$$S_2 = 1 \cdot 1! + 2 \cdot 2! = 5,$$
$$S_3 = 1 \cdot 1! + 2 \cdot 2! + 3 \cdot 3! = 23,$$
$$S_4 = 1 \cdot 1! + 2 \cdot 2! + 3 \cdot 3! + 4 \cdot 4! = 119.$$

Looking closely at these results we observe that

$$S_1 = 2! - 1, \quad S_2 = 3! - 1, \quad S_3 = 4! - 1, \quad S_4 = 5! - 1.$$

This suggests the hypothesis:

$$S_n = (n+1)! - 1.$$

Let us check this hypothesis.

T h e o r e m   1.   For $n = 1$ the hypothesis is correct, as

$$S_1 = 1 \cdot 1! = 2! - 1.$$

T h e o r e m   2.   Let

$$S_k = 1 \cdot 1! + 2 \cdot 2! + \ldots + k \cdot k! = (k+1)! - 1.$$

To show that

$$S_{k+1} = 1 \cdot 1! + 2 \cdot 2! + \ldots + k \cdot k! + (k+1) \cdot (k+1)! =$$
$$= (k+2)! - 1,$$

we observe that

$$S_{k+1} = S_k + (k+1) \cdot (k+1)! =$$
$$= [(k+1)! - 1] + (k+1) \cdot (k+1)! =$$
$$= (k+1)! [1 + (k+1)] - 1 =$$
$$= (k+1)! (k+2) - 1 = (k+2)! - 1.$$

Problem 21. Prove the identity

$$\frac{1}{1+x} + \frac{2}{1+x^2} + \frac{4}{1+x^4} + \frac{8}{1+x^8} + \cdots + \frac{2^n}{1+x^{2^n}} =$$

$$= \frac{1}{x-1} + \frac{2^{n+1}}{1-x^{2^{n+1}}}.$$

Problem 22. It is given that

$$\alpha + \beta = m, \quad \alpha\beta = a, \quad A_2 = m - \frac{a}{m-1},$$

$$A_3 = m - \frac{a}{m - \dfrac{a}{m-1}}, \quad A_4 = m - \frac{a}{m - \dfrac{a}{m - \dfrac{a}{m-1}}},$$

and so on, that is, for $k > 1$

$$A_{k+1} = m - \frac{a}{A_k} \qquad (m \neq 1; \quad \alpha \neq \beta).$$

Prove that

$$A_n = \frac{(\alpha^{n+1} - \beta^{n+1}) - (\alpha^n - \beta^n)}{(\alpha^n - \beta^n) - (\alpha^{n-1} - \beta^{n-1})}. \tag{1}$$

Solution

Theorem 1. To begin with, we shall prove that formula (1) is true for $n = 2$. From the given condition it follows that

$$A_2 = m - \frac{a}{m-1} = (\alpha + \beta) - \frac{\alpha\beta}{(\alpha+\beta)-1} = \frac{\alpha^2 + \beta^2 + \alpha\beta - \alpha - \beta}{\alpha + \beta - 1}.$$

According to formula (1)

$$A_2 = \frac{(\alpha^3 - \beta^3) - (\alpha^2 - \beta^2)}{(\alpha^2 - \beta^2) - (\alpha - \beta)}.$$

Dividing the top and bottom of the latter fraction by $\alpha - \beta$, we have

$$A_2 = \frac{\alpha^2 + \beta^2 + \alpha\beta - \alpha - \beta}{\alpha + \beta - 1},$$

which was what we set out to prove.

T h e o r e m 2. Suppose that formula (1) is valid for $n = k$, i.e. that

$$A_k = \frac{(\alpha^{k+1} - \beta^{k+1}) - (\alpha^k - \beta^k)}{(\alpha^k - \beta^k) - (\alpha^{k-1} - \beta^{k-1})}.$$

(2)

We shall prove, that in that case it is valid also for $n = k+1$, i.e.

$$A_{k+1} = \frac{(\alpha^{k+2} - \beta^{k+2}) - (\alpha^{k+1} - \beta^{k+1})}{(\alpha^{k+1} - \beta^{k+1}) - (\alpha^k - \beta^k)}.$$

Now

$$A_{k+1} = m - \frac{a}{A_k} \quad \text{or} \quad A_{k+1} = (\alpha + \beta) - \frac{\alpha\beta}{A_k}.$$

Making use of equation (2) we find that

$$A_{k+1} = (\alpha + \beta) - \frac{\alpha\beta \left[(\alpha^k - \beta^k) - (\alpha^{k-1} - \beta^{k-1}) \right]}{(\alpha^{k+1} - \beta^{k+1}) - (\alpha^k - \beta^k)} =$$

$$= \frac{(\alpha^{k+2} - \beta^{k+2}) - (\alpha^{k+1} - \beta^{k+1})}{(\alpha^{k+1} - \beta^{k+1}) - (\alpha^k - \beta^k)}.$$

so that the theorem is proved.

Problem 23. Simplify the polynomial

$$1 - \frac{x}{1!} + \frac{x(x-1)}{2!} - \ldots + (-1)^n \frac{x(x-1)\ldots(x-n+1)}{n!}.$$

A n s w e r.

$$(-1)^n \frac{(x-1)(x-2)\ldots(x-n)}{n!}.$$

Problem 24. Prove that it is possible to pay, without requiring change, any whole number of roubles, greater than 7, with banknotes of value 3 roubles and 5 roubles.

S o l u t i o n. For 8 roubles the statement is true. Let the statement be true for k roubles where k is an integer greater than or equal to 8.

Two cases are possible:

(a) k roubles being paid with three-rouble banknotes only and

(b) k roubles being paid with banknotes among which there is at least one of value 5 roubles.

In case (a) there must be not less than three 3-rouble notes, as in this case $k > 8$. To pay $k+1$ roubles we should exchange three 3-rouble notes for two 5-rouble notes.

In the second case, to pay $k+1$ roubles, we should exchange one 5-rouble note for two 3-rouble ones.

Problem 25. Prove that the sum of the cubes of three successive positive integers is divisible by 9.

S o l u t i o n. The sum $1^3 + 2^3 + 3^3$ is divisible by 9. This means, that the statement is correct when the first of the three successive natural numbers is 1.

Let the sum $k^3 + (k+1)^3 + (k+2)^3$, where k is some natural number, be divisible by 9. The sum

$$(k+1)^3 + (k+2)^3 + (k+3)^3 =$$
$$= [k^3 + (k+1)^3 + (k+2)^3] + 9(k^2 + 3k + 3)$$

can be written as the sum of two terms each of which is divisible by 9. It is therefore also divisible by 9 and the result is established.

Problem 26. Prove that for a whole $n \geqslant 0$

$$A_n = 11^{n+2} + 12^{2n+1}$$

is divisible by 133.

Problem 27. $n+1$ numbers are picked at random from the $2n$ integers 1, 2, ... $2n$. Prove that among the numbers picked we can find at least two, one of which is divisible by the other.

S o l u t i o n. Let us suppose, that out of the numbers 1, 2, ... $2n$, where $n \geqslant 2$, we managed to pick $n+1$ numbers in such a way that none of them is divisible by any other. We shall denote the set of all these numbers by M_{n+1}. We shall prove that in that case it is possible to pick n numbers out of the $2n-2$ numbers: 1, 2, $\ldots$ $2n-2$, such that again none is divisible by any other. Four cases can arise.

(a) M_{n+1} contains neither $2n-1$ nor $2n$.

(b) M_{n+1} contains $2n-1$ but not $2n$.

(c) M_{n+1} contains $2n$ but not $2n-1$.

(d) M_{n+1} contains both $2n-1$ and $2n$.

C a s e (a): Let us exclude any one number from M_{n+1}. n numbers will remain, none of which is greater than $2n-2$. None of these numbers is divisible by any other.

C a s e (b): Let us exclude the number $2n-1$ from M_{n+1}. n numbers remain, none of which is greater than $2n-2$. None of these numbers is divisible by any other.

C a s e (c): Let us exclude $2n$ from M_{n+1} and again we obtain the same result.

C a s e (d): First of all let us note that M_{n+1} cannot contain the number n, otherwise there would have been two numbers ($2n$ and n) one of which is divisible by the other. Let us exclude $2n-1$ and $2n$. We shall denote the remaining set of $n-1$ numbers by M_{n-1}. Let us now join the number n to M_{n-1}. We obtain n numbers, none of which is greater than $2n-2$. It remains to show that among these numbers none is divisible by any other.

In M_{n+1} there were no numbers divisible one by the other. This means, that there were no such numbers in M_{n-1} either. It remains only to make sure that no such numbers appeared when n joined M_{n-1}.

For this purpose it is sufficient to make sure that:

(1) None of the numbers making up M_{n-1} is divisible by n and

(2) the number n is not divisible by any of the numbers in M_{n-1}.

The former follows from the fact that none of the numbers in M_{n-1} is greater than $2n-2$. The latter follows from the fact that $2n$ is indivisible by any of the numbers making up M_{n-1}.

Thus, if it supposed that the proposition is wrong for the $2n$ numbers 1, 2, ...$2n$, it is also wrong for the $2(n-1)$ numbers 1, 2, ... $2n-2$. That means, if the proposition is correct for the $2(n-1)$ numbers 1, 2, ... $2n -2$, that it is correct also for the $2n$ numbers 1, 2, ... $2n$.

For the two numbers 1, 2 the proposition is true. That means, that the proposition is true for the $2n$ numbers 1, 2, ...$2n$, where n is any natural number.

We should note that this problem has the following simple solution. Let us pick any $n+1$ numbers out of the $2n$ numbers 1, 2, ...$2n$. Let us denote this set of numbers by M_{n+1}.

We shall divide each even number in M_{n+1} by such a power of 2 that the quotient is odd. Out of these quotients and odd numbers we shall make up the set M_{n+1}. In M_{n+1} there are $n+1$ odd numbers, each of which is less than $2n$.

As there are, in all, n positive odd numbers less than $2n$ $\overline{M}_{n+1}$ must contain at least two equal numbers. Let us denote each of these equal numbers by k.

This result means that in M_{n+1} there were at least two numbers $2^s k$ and $2^t k$. One is divisible by the other.

<u>Problem 28</u>. Prove that n various straight lines in a plane, passing through one point, divide the plane into $2n$ parts.

<u>Problem 29</u>. Prove that n straight lines lying in a plane break up the plane into parts, which it is possible to paint with black and white paint in such a way, that all adjacent parts (i.e. parts which have a segment of a straight line in common) are painted in different colours.

2

<u>Problem 30</u>. Prove that n plane, passing through one point in such a way that no three of them pass through the same straight line divide space into $A_n = n(n-1)+2$ parts.

S o l u t i o n. (1) One plane divides space into 2 parts
and $A_1 = 2$. For $n = 1$, the proposition is therefore correct.

(2) Let us suppose that the proposition is justified for
$n = k$, i.e. k planes divide space into $k(k-1)+2$ parts.
We shall then prove that $k+1$ planes divide space into
$k(k+1)+2$ parts.

Let P be the $(k+1)$ th plane. The plane P is intersected
by each of the first k planes along some straight line. In
this way the plane P is divided into parts by k different
straight lines, which pass through one point. Taking Problem 28 as the basis of our argument we state that the plane
P is broken up into $2k$ parts, each of which represents a
plane angle with its apex at the given point.

The first k planes divide space into certain polyhedral
angles.

Some of these polyhedral angles are divided by plane P
into two parts.

The common face of two such parts is a part of the plane
limited by the two rays along which P intersects the faces
of the particular polyhedral angle, i.e. it is one of the
$2k$ plane angles into which the plane P was broken up.

This means that the number of polyhedral angles which are
broken into two parts by the plane P cannot be greater than
$2k$.

On the other hand, each of the $2k$ parts into which the
plane P is divided as a result of its intersection with the
first k planes is a common face of two polyhedral angles
and so it divides the polyhedral angle formed by the first
k planes into two parts.

This means that the number of polyhedral angles which are
broken into two parts by the plane P cannot be less than
$2k$.

Thus, the plane P breaks up into two parts exactly $2k$
parts of space formed by the first k planes. If k planes,
therefore, break space up into $k(k-1)+2$ parts, then $k+1$
planes break space up into

$$[k(k-1)+2]+2k = k(k+1)+2$$

parts. The proposition is therefore proved.

Problem 31. Prove the identity

$$\cos \alpha \cos 2\alpha \cos 4\alpha \ldots \cos 2^n \alpha = \frac{\sin 2^{n+1} \alpha}{2^{n+1} \sin \alpha}.$$

S o l u t i o n. (1) For $n = 0$ the identity is true as

$$\cos \alpha = \frac{\sin 2\alpha}{2 \sin \alpha}.$$

(2) Suppose the identity to be true for $n = k$, i.e.

$$\cos \alpha \cos 2\alpha \ldots \cos 2^k \alpha = \frac{\sin 2^{k+1} \alpha}{2^{k+1} \sin \alpha}.$$

Then it is also true for $n = k+1$. For

$$\cos \alpha \cos 2\alpha \ldots \cos 2^k \alpha \cos 2^{k+1} \alpha =$$
$$= \frac{\sin 2^{k+1} \alpha \cos 2^{k+1} \alpha}{2^{k+1} \sin \alpha} = \frac{\sin 2^{k+2} \alpha}{2^{k+2} \sin \alpha}.$$

Problem 32. Prove that $A_n = \cos n\theta$, if it is given that $A_1 = \cos \theta$, $A_2 = \cos 2\theta$, and for an integer $k > 2$ there exists the following relationship

$$A_k = 2 \cos \theta A_{k-1} - A_{k-2}.$$

S o l u t i o n. (1) The proposition is true for $n = 1$ and for $n = 2$.
(2) Let

$$A_{k-2} = \cos(k-2)\theta, \quad A_{k-1} = \cos(k-1)\theta.$$

Then

$$A_k = 2 \cos \theta \cos(k-1)\theta - \cos(k-2)\theta = \cos k\theta.$$

Problem 33. Prove that

$$\sin x + \sin 2x + \ldots + \sin nx = \frac{\sin \frac{n+1}{2} x}{\sin \frac{x}{2}} \sin \frac{nx}{2}.$$

S o l u t i o n. (1) For $n = 1$ the proposition is correct.

(2) Let

$$\sin x + \sin 2x + \ldots + \sin kx = \frac{\sin \frac{k+1}{2} x}{\sin \frac{x}{2}} \sin \frac{kx}{2}.$$

Then

$$\sin x + \sin 2x + \ldots + \sin kx + \sin (k+1) x =$$

$$= \frac{\sin \frac{k+1}{2} x}{\sin \frac{x}{2}} \sin \frac{kx}{2} + \sin (k+1) x =$$

$$= \frac{\sin \frac{k+1}{2} x}{\sin \frac{x}{2}} \sin \frac{kx}{2} + 2 \sin \frac{k+1}{2} x \cos \frac{k+1}{2} x = \frac{\sin \frac{k+2}{2} x}{\sin \frac{x}{2}} \sin \frac{k+1}{2} x,$$

because

$$2 \cos \frac{k+1}{2} x \sin \frac{x}{2} = \sin \frac{k+2}{2} x - \sin \frac{kx}{2}.$$

<u>Problem 34.</u> Prove that

$$\frac{1}{2} + \cos x + \cos 2x + \ldots + \cos nx = \frac{\sin \frac{2n+1}{2} x}{2 \sin \frac{x}{2}}.$$

<u>Problem 35.</u> Prove that

$$\sin x + 2 \sin 2x + 3 \sin 3x + \ldots + n \sin nx =$$

$$= \frac{(n+1) \sin nx - n \sin (n+1) x}{4 \sin^2 \frac{x}{2}}.$$

<u>Problem 36.</u> Prove that

$$\cos x + 2 \cos 2x + \ldots + n \cos nx =$$

$$= \frac{(n+1) \cos nx - n \cos (n+1) x - 1}{4 \sin^2 \frac{x}{2}}.$$

<u>Problem 37.</u> Prove that

$$\frac{1}{2} \tan \frac{x}{2} + \frac{1}{2^2} \tan \frac{x}{2^2} + \ldots + \frac{1}{2^n} \tan \frac{x}{2^n} =$$

$$= \frac{1}{2^n} \cot \frac{x}{2^n} - \cot x \qquad (x \neq m\pi).$$

<u>Problem 38.</u> Prove that

$$\cot^{-1} 3 + \cot^{-1} 5 + \ldots + \cot^{-1} (2n+1) =$$

$$= \tan^{-1} 2 + \tan^{-1} \frac{3}{2} + \ldots + \tan^{-1} \frac{n+1}{n} - n \tan^{-1} 1.$$

<u>Problem 39</u>. Prove that

$$(1+i)^n = 2^{\frac{n}{2}}\left(\cos\frac{n\pi}{4} + i\sin\frac{n\pi}{4}\right).$$

S o l u t i o n. (1) For $n=1$, the proposition is true, as

$$1+i = 2^{\frac{1}{2}}\left(\cos\frac{\pi}{4} + i\sin\frac{\pi}{4}\right).$$

(2) Let

$$(1+i)^k = 2^{\frac{k}{2}}\left(\cos\frac{k\pi}{4} + i\sin\frac{k\pi}{4}\right).$$

Then

$$(1+i)^{k+1} =$$

$$= 2^{\frac{k}{2}}\left(\cos\frac{k\pi}{4} + i\sin\frac{k\pi}{4}\right)\cdot 2^{\frac{1}{2}}\left(\cos\frac{\pi}{4} + i\sin\frac{\pi}{4}\right) =$$

$$= 2^{\frac{k+1}{2}}\left(\cos\frac{(k+1)\pi}{4} + i\sin\frac{(k+1)\pi}{4}\right).$$

<u>Problem 40</u>. Prove that

$$(\sqrt{3}-i)^n = 2^n\left(\cos\frac{n\pi}{6} - i\sin\frac{n\pi}{6}\right).$$

<u>Problem 41</u>. Prove the following theorem.

If, as a result of a finite number of rational operations (i.e. addition, subtraction, multiplication and division) carried out with the complex numbers $x_1, x_2, \ldots, x_n$, we obtain the number u, the result of the same operations carried out with the conjugate complex numbers $\bar{x}_1, \bar{x}_2, \ldots, \bar{x}_n$ will be $\bar{u}$, the conjugate of u.

S o l u t i o n. We shall show, first of all, that the proposition is correct for each of the four operations carried out with 2 complex numbers. Let

$$x_1 = a+bi, \quad x_2 = c+di.$$

Then

$$x_1 + x_2 = (a+c) + (b+d)i = u;$$
$$\bar{x}_1 + \bar{x}_2 = (a-bi) + (c-di) = (a+c) - (b+d)i = \bar{u}.$$

The proposition is verified in exactly the same way for subtraction, multiplication and division.

Now, let us be given some rational expression involving complex numbers $x_1, x_2, \ldots, x_n$. The calculation of such an expression reduces to the carrying out, step by step, of one operation with two complex numbers at a time. These operations can be numbered.

For example, let

$$u = \frac{x_1 x_2 + x_3 x_4}{x_1 + x_2 - x_3}.$$

To calculate u it is sufficient to carry out the following operations:

1)	$x_1 x_2 = u_1,$	4)	$u_3 - x_3 = u_4,$
2)	$x_3 x_4 = u_2,$	5)	$u_1 + u_2 = u_5,$
3)	$x_1 + x_2 = u_3,$	6)	$u_5 : u_4 = u.$

Let us suppose that the proposition is correct for all expressions for whose calculation no more than k operations are required. The term 'operation' means here either addition, subtraction, multiplication or division of two complex numbers. We shall show that, in that case, the proposition should also be true for expressions requiring $k+1$ operations.

Indeed, the last $(k+1)$th operation was carried out on the numbers u_i and u_j, which themselves were calculated by means of no more than k operations.

As a result of the substitution of numbers $x_1, x_2, \ldots, x_n$ by their conjugates the numbers u_i and u_j are replaced by the conjugates $\bar{u}_i$ and $\bar{u}_j$ and then also the result of the $(k+1)$th operation on them, i.e. the number $u,$ is replaced by its conjugate $\bar{u}$.

<u>Problem 42</u>. Prove that for any positive integer n

$$(\cos x + i \sin x)^n = \cos nx + i \sin nx.$$

<u>Problem 43</u>. Prove that for any positive integer $n > 1$

$$\frac{1}{n+1} + \frac{1}{n+2} + \cdots + \frac{1}{2n} > \frac{13}{24}.$$

S o l u t i o n. For convenience we denote the left-hand side of the equation by S_n.

(1) Since $S_2 = \frac{7}{12} = \frac{14}{24}$, it follows that for $n = 2$ the inequality holds.

(2) Suppose that $S_k > \frac{13}{24}$ for some k. We shall prove that in that case also $S_{k+1} > \frac{13}{24}$. We have

$$S_k = \frac{1}{k+1} + \frac{1}{k+2} + \cdots + \frac{1}{2k},$$
$$S_{k+1} = \frac{1}{k+2} + \frac{1}{k+3} + \cdots + \frac{1}{2k} +$$
$$+ \frac{1}{2k+1} + \frac{1}{2k+2}.$$

Comparing S_k with S_{k+1} we have

$$S_{k+1} - S_k = \frac{1}{2k+1} + \frac{1}{2k+2} - \frac{1}{k+1},$$

i.e.

$$S_{k+1} - S_k = \frac{1}{2(k+1)(2k+1)}.$$

For any positive integer k the right-hand side of the last equation is positive. Therefore $S_{k+1} > S_k$. . But $S_k > \frac{13}{24}$, , which proves that $S_{k+1} > \frac{13}{24}$.

<u>Problem 44</u>. Find the error in the following proof.

P r o p o s i t i o n. For any positive integer n the following inequality holds:

$$2^n > 2n + 1.$$

P r o o f: Let the inequality be justified for $n = k$,

where k is some natural number, i.e.

$$2^k > 2k + 1. \tag{1}$$

We shall prove that then the inequality is justified also for $n = k + 1$, i.e.

$$2^{k+1} > 2(k+1) + 1. \tag{2}$$

And really, 2^k is not less than 2 for any natural k . Let us add 2^k to the left-hand side of the inequality (1), and add 2 to the right-hand side of that inequality. We obtain the correct inequality

$$2^k + 2^k > 2k + 1 + 2,$$

or

$$2^{k+1} > 2(k+1) + 1.$$

The proposition is therefore proved.

Problem 45. For which natural n does the following inequality hold true:

$$2^n > 2n + 1 ?$$

Problem 46. For which positive integers n is the following inequality valid:

$$2^n > n^2 ?$$

Solution.

For $n = 1$ the inequality is true, as $2^1 > 1^2$.

For $n = 2$ the inequality is false, as $2^2 = 2^2$.

For $n = 3$ the inequality is false, as $2^3 < 3^2$.

For $n = 4$ the inequality is false, as $2^4 = 4^2$.

For $n = 5$ the inequality is true, as $2^5 > 5^2$.

For $n = 6$ the inequality is true, as $2^6 > 6^2$.

It would seem that the inequality is true for $n = 1$ and for any $n > 4$. Let us prove it.

(1) For $n = 5$ the inequality holds.

(2) Let

$$2^k > k^2, \tag{1}$$

where k is some positive integer greater than 4.

We shall prove that

$$2^{k+1} > (k+1)^2. \tag{2}$$

We know that $2^k > 2k + 1$ for $k > 4$ (Problem 45). Therefore, if we add 2^k to the left-hand side of the inequality and $2k + 1$ to its right-hand side, we shall obtain the true inequality (2).

A n s w e r. $2^n > n^2$ when $n = 1$ and when $n > 4$.

Problem 47. Prove that

$$(1 + \alpha)^n > 1 + n\alpha,$$

where $\alpha > -1$, $\alpha \neq 0$, n is a positive integer greater than 1.

S o l u t i o n. (1) For $n = 2$, the inequality holds (since $\alpha^2 > 0$).

(2) Let the inequality hold when $n = k$, where k is some positive integer, i.e.

$$(1 + \alpha)^k > 1 + k\alpha. \tag{1}$$

We shall show that in that case the inequality holds also for $n = k + 1$, i.e. we shall show that

$$(1 + \alpha)^{k+1} > 1 + (k+1)\alpha. \tag{2}$$

Indeed, it follows from the conditions of the problem that $1+\alpha>0$, so that the following inequality holds:

$$(1+\alpha)^{k+1} > (1+k\alpha)(1+\alpha), \tag{3}$$

This inequality is obtained from (1) by multiplying both sides by $1+\alpha$. We can rewrite the inequality (3) in the form

$$(1+\alpha)^{k+1} > 1+(k+1)\alpha+k\alpha^2.$$

Neglecting the positive term $k\alpha^2$ on the right-hand side we find that the inequality (2) is established.

<u>Problem 48</u>.   Prove that for any positive integer $n>1$

$$\frac{1}{\sqrt{1}}+\frac{1}{\sqrt{2}}+\cdots+\frac{1}{\sqrt{n}} > \sqrt{n}.$$

<u>Problem 49</u>.   Prove that for any positive integer $n>1$

$$\frac{4^n}{n+1} < \frac{(2n)!}{(n!)^2}.$$

<u>Problem 50</u>.   Prove that

$$2^{n-1}(a^n+b^n) > (a+b)^n, \tag{1}$$

where $a+b>0$, $a \neq b$, and n is a positive integer greater than unity.

S o l u t i o n.   1) When $n=2$, the inequality (1) takes the form

$$2(a^2+b^2) > (a+b)^2. \tag{2}$$

As $a \neq b$, the following inequality holds

$$(a-b)^2 > 0. \tag{3}$$

Adding $(a+b)^2$ to each side of the inequality (3) we obtain the inequality (2).

Thus, it is proved that the inequality (1) is true for $n = 2$.

2) Suppose that the inequality (1) holds for $n = k$ where k is some positive integer, i.e. suppose that

$$2^{k-1}(a^k + b^k) > (a + b)^k. \qquad (4)$$

We shall prove that, in that case, the inequality (1) holds also for $n = k + 1$, i.e.

$$2^k(a^{k+1} + b^{k+1}) > (a + b)^{k+1}. \qquad (5)$$

Let us multiply both sides of the inequality (4) by $a + b$. Since it is given that $a + b > 0$, we obtain the following correct inequality:

$$2^{k-1}(a^k + b^k)(a + b) > (a + b)^{k+1}. \qquad (6)$$

To prove the truth of the inequality (5) it is sufficient to show that

$$2^k(a^{k+1} + b^{k+1}) > 2^{k-1}(a^k + b^k)(a + b), \qquad (7)$$

or, what is the same thing, that

$$a^{k+1} + b^{k+1} > a^k b + a b^k. \qquad (8)$$

The inequality (8) can be rewritten in the form

$$(a^k - b^k)(a - b) > 0. \qquad (9)$$

Suppose that $a > b$. As, in addition to that, it is given that $a > -b$, we have $a > |b|$ and it follows that $a^k > b^k$ On the left-hand side of the inequality (9) we have a product of two positive numbers, which is, of course, positive.

If $a < b$, using the same arguments, we establish that $a^k < b^k$. In this case we have a product of two negative numbers on the left-hand side of the inequality (9), and this too is positive.

In both cases therefore the inequality (9) is valid.

This proves, that the truth of the inequality (1) for $n = k + 1$ follows from its truth for $n = k$.

Problem 51. Prove that for any $x > 0$, and any positive integer n the following inequality holds

$$x^n + x^{n-2} + x^{n-4} + \ldots + \frac{1}{x^{n-4}} + \frac{1}{x^{n-2}} + \frac{1}{x^n} \geqslant n + 1. \qquad (1)$$

S o l u t i o n. 1a) For $n = 1$ the inequality (1) takes the form

$$x + \frac{1}{x} \geqslant 2. \qquad (2)$$

The inequality (2) stems from the obvious inequality

$$(x - 1)^2 \geqslant 0.$$

1b) For $n = 2$ the inequality (1) takes the form

$$x^2 + 1 + \frac{1}{x^2} \geqslant 3. \qquad (3)$$

The inequality (2) holds for any $x > 0$. This means that it also holds when x is substituted for x^2, i.e.

$$x^2 + \frac{1}{x^2} \geqslant 2.$$

Adding 1 to both sides of this inequality we obtain the inequality (3).

2) Suppose that the inequality (1) holds for $n = k$, where k is some positive integer, i.e.

$$x^k + x^{k-2} + \ldots + \frac{1}{x^{k-2}} + \frac{1}{x^k} \geqslant k + 1. \qquad (4)$$

We shall prove that, in that case, the inequality (1) also holds for $n = k + 2$, i.e.

$$x^{k+2} + x^k + x^{k-2} + \ldots + \frac{1}{x^{k-2}} + \frac{1}{x^k} + \frac{1}{x^{k+2}} \geqslant k + 3. \qquad (5)$$

Substituting x^{k+2} for x in the inequality (2) we get

$$x^{k+2} + \frac{1}{x^{k+2}} \geqslant 2. \tag{6}$$

Adding together the left-hand sides of the inequalities (4) and (6) and then their right-hand sides we obtain the inequality (5).

Now, let us sum up.

In the subsections 1a) and 1b) we proved that the inequality (1) is valid for $n = 1$ and $n = 2$.

In subsection 2) we proved that the truth of the inequality (1) for $n = k + 2$ is a consequence of the truth of that inequality for $n = k$. In other words, subsection 2) gives us the right to pass from $n = k$ to $n = k + 2$.

The results of subsection 1a) and 2) gives us the right to state that the inequality (1) is true for any odd integer n. Exactly in the same way the results of subsections 1b) and 2) give us the right to state that the inequality (1) is true for any even integer n. On the whole, we can state that the inequality (1) is true for any positive integer n.

Problem 52. Prove the following theorem.

The geometric mean of several positive numbers is not greater than their arithmetic mean, i.e. if $a_1, a_2, \ldots, a_n$ are positive, then

$$\sqrt[n]{a_1 a_2 \ldots a_n} \leqslant \frac{a_1 + a_2 + \ldots + a_n}{n}. \tag{1}$$

S o l u t i o n. 1) For $n = 2$ the inequality (1) takes the simple form

$$\sqrt{a_1 a_2} \leqslant \frac{a_1 + a_2}{2}. \tag{2}$$

For any positive a_1 and a_2, we have the following inequality

$$(\sqrt{a_1} - \sqrt{a_2})^2 \geqslant 0.$$

From which it is easy to obtain inequality (2).

The inequality (2) has a simple geometrical meaning. On the straight line AB mark off segments of length a_1 and a_2 consecutively. Using their sum as a diameter describe a circle. Then $\frac{a_1+a_2}{2}$ is the diameter of that circle, and $\sqrt{a_1a_2}$ is half the chord which is perpendicular to that diameter at the point common to a_1 and a_2. The inequality (2) states that no chord of a circle has a length greater than the diameter.

2) Let us suppose that inequality (1) is true for $n=k$.

We shall prove that in that case it is true also for $n=2k$. This follows from

$$\sqrt[2k]{a_1a_2\ldots a_{2k}}=\sqrt[k]{\sqrt[k]{a_1a_2\ldots a_k}\cdot\sqrt[k]{a_{k+1}\ldots a_{2k}}}\leqslant$$
$$\leqslant\frac{\sqrt[k]{a_1a_2\ldots a_k}+\sqrt[k]{a_{k+1}\ldots a_{2k}}}{2}\leqslant$$
$$\leqslant\frac{\frac{a_1+a_2+\ldots+a_k}{k}+\frac{a_{k+1}+\ldots+a_{2k}}{k}}{2}=$$
$$=\frac{a_1+a_2+\ldots+a_k+\ldots+a_{2k}}{2k}.$$

The inequality (1) has been verified for $n=2$ and using this last result we can now assert that it is true for $n = 4, 8, 16$ and so on, i.e. in general for $n=2^s$, where s is a positive integer.

3) To establish the truth of the inequality (1) for any positive integer n, we shall show that it follows from the truth of the inequality for $n=k$ that it is true also for $n=k-1$.

To do this, let $a_1, a_2, \ldots, a_{k-1}$ denote positive numbers. Let λ be some positive number (for the present unknown). Then

$$\sqrt[k]{a_1a_2\ldots a_{k-1}\lambda}\leqslant\frac{a_1+a_2+\ldots+a_{k-1}+\lambda}{k}.$$

We shall choose λ in such a way that

$$\frac{a_1+a_2+\ldots+a_{k-1}+\lambda}{k}=\frac{a_1+a_2+\ldots+a_{k-1}}{k-1},$$

i.e. we shall make

$$\lambda = \frac{a_1 + a_2 + \ldots + a_{k-1}}{k - 1}.$$

We have

$$\sqrt[k]{\frac{a_1 a_2 \ldots a_{k-1} (a_1 + a_2 + \ldots + a_{k-1})}{k - 1}} \leqslant \frac{a_1 + a_2 + \ldots + a_{k-1}}{k - 1},$$

or

$$\sqrt[k-1]{a_1 a_2 \ldots a_{k-1}} \leqslant \frac{a_1 + a_2 + \ldots + a_{k-1}}{k - 1}.$$

Now, let m be any natural number. If $m = 2^s$, then according to (2) the inequality holds for it. If on the other hand $m \neq 2^s$, we shall find such an s, that m is less than 2^s, and then, on the basis of (2) and (3), we state that the inequality is correct for $n = m$.

THE PROOF BY INDUCTION OF SOME THEOREMS OF ELEMENTARY ALGEBRA

T h e o r e m 1. <u>The square of a polynomial is equal to the sum of the squares of all its terms added to twice all possible products of the terms taken two at a time, i.e.</u>

$$(a_1 + a_2 + \ldots + a_n)^2 = a_1^2 + a_2^2 + \ldots + a_n^2 + \\ + 2\,(a_1 a_2 + a_1 a_3 + \ldots + a_{n-1} a_n). \tag{1}$$

For $n = 2$ the formula (1) can be proved by direct multiplication.

Suppose that the formula (1) is true for $n = k-1$, i.e. that

$$(a_1 + a_2 + \ldots + a_{k-1})^2 = a_1^2 + a_2^2 + \ldots + a_{k-1}^2 + 2S,$$

where S is the sum of all possible products of $a_1, a_2, \ldots, a_{k-1}$, taken two at a time. We shall prove that

$$(a_1 + a_2 + \ldots + a_{k-1} + a_k)^2 = \\ = a_1^2 + a_2^2 + \ldots + a_{k-1}^2 + a_k^2 + 2S_1,$$

where S_1 is the sum of all the possible products taken two at a time of $a_1, a_2, \ldots, a_{k-1}, a_k$, i.e.

$$S_1 = S + (a_1 + a_2 + \ldots + a_{k-1}) a_k$$

This follows from the fact that

$$(a_1 + \ldots + a_{k-1} + a_k)^2 = [(a_1 + \ldots + a_{k-1}) + a_k]^2 = \\ = (a_1 + \ldots + a_{k-1})^2 + 2\,(a_1 + \ldots + a_{k-1})\,a_k + a_k^2 = \\ = a_1^2 + \ldots + a_{k-1}^2 + 2S + 2\,(a_1 + \ldots + a_{k-1})\,a_k + a_k^2 = \\ = a_1^2 + a_2^2 + \ldots + a_k^2 + 2S_1$$

T h e o r e m 2. **The nth term of an arithmetic progression can be calculated according to the formula**

$$a_n = a_1 + d(n-1) \qquad (1)$$

where a_1 is the first term and d is the common difference.

For $n = 1$, the formula (1) is correct.

Suppose that formula (1) is correct for $n = k$, i.e.

$$a_k = a_1 + d(k-1)$$

Then

$$a_{k+1} = a_k + d = a_1 + d(k-1) + d = a_1 + dk,$$

i.e. formula (1) turned out to be correct also for $n = k+1$.

T h e o r e m 3. **The nth term of a geometric progression can be calculated according to the formula**

$$a_n = a_1 q^{n-1}, \qquad (1)$$

where a_1 is the first term, and q is the common ratio of the progression.

For $n = 1$ the formula (1) is correct.

Let

$$a_k = a_1 q^{k-1}.$$

Then

$$a_{k+1} = a_k q = a_1 q^k.$$

T h e o r e m 4. **The number of permutations of m elements can be calculated according to the formula**

$$P_m = m! \qquad (1)$$

First of all, we shall note, that $P_1 = 1$ and thus the formula (1) is correct for $m = 1$.

Suppose that $P_k = k!$ We shall prove that

$$P_{k+1} = (k+1)!$$

We shall just take the first k out of the following $k+1$ elements $a_1, a_2, \ldots, a_k, a_{k+1}$ and form all the possible permutations out of them. According to the condition above, there will be $k!$ such permutations.

Into each of these permutations we shall put the element a_{k+1}, consecutively before the 1st element, before the 2nd ......, before the kth and after the kth. In this way we· shall obtain $k+1$ permutations of $k+1$ elements out of one permutation of k elements. Altogether we have

$$k!(k+1) = (k+1)!$$

permutations out of $k+1$ elements. It is necessary to make clear the following:

1) whether there are any two identical ones among the $(k+1)!$ permutations;

2) whether we obtained all possible permutations of $k+1$ elements.

1) Suppose that there are two identical ones among the $(k+1)!$ permutations. Let us call them p_1 and p_2. In the permutation p_1 let the element a_{k+1} occupy the sth place counting from the left. Then in p_2 the elements a_{k+1} will also occupy the sth place counting from the left.

Let us remove the element a_{k+1} from p_1 and from p_2. We shall obtain two identical permutations of k elements - $\overline{p_1}$ and $\overline{p_2}$. That means, that to obtain p_1 and p_2 the element a_{k+1} was put twice into the same place in the same permutation of elements $a_1, a_2, \ldots, a_k$. This contradicts the rule, according to which permutations are built up.

2) Suppose that a certain permutation p of $k+1$ elements has not been obtained. Let element a_{k+1} occupy the sth place from the left in p.

Remove the element a_{k+1} from p . We obtain the permutation $\bar{p}$ of the first k elements. This means that to obtain p it was sufficient to take the permutation $\bar{p}$ and put the element a_{k+1} into it in such a way that it takes up the sth position from the left. We could not avoid taking the permutation $\bar{p}$, as we were taking all possible permutations of the first k elements. We could not avoid putting the element a_{k+1} into the position indicated as we were putting it first, second, ... and $(k+1)$th from the left.

Thus, the permutations which we have formed are all different and every possible permutation of $k+1$ elements has been obtained.

It follows from the above that

$$P_{k+1} = (k+1)!$$

T h e o r e m 5. <u>The number of permutations of m elements taken n at a time can be calculated according to the formula</u>

$$^nP_m = m(m-1) \ldots (m-n+1). \tag{1}$$

First of all we shall note, that $^1P_m = m$ and thus the formula (1) is true for $n=1$. Suppose that

$$^kP_m = m(m-1) \ldots (m-k+1),$$

where $k < m$. We shall prove that

$$^{k+1}P_m = m(m-1) \ldots (m-k).$$

To obtain all permutations of m elements, $k+1$ at a time, it is sufficient to take all permutations of m elements k at a time, and add on to each of them every one of the remaining $m-k$ elements.

It is easy to convince ourselves that the permutations of m elements, $k+1$ at a time, built up in this way are all different, and, apart from that, that every permutation of m elements, $k+1$ at a time, is present in those obtained.

It turns out that

$$^{k+1}P_m = {}^k P_m (m - k) = m (m - 1) \ldots (m - k).$$

Theorem 6. The number of combinations of m elements taken n at a time can be calculated according to the formula

$$^n C_m = \frac{m (m-1) \ldots (m-n+1)}{1 \cdot 2 \ldots n}. \tag{1}$$

First of all we shall note that $^1 C_m = m$, and therefore formula (1) is correct for $n = 1$.

Suppose that

$$^k C_m = \frac{m (m-1) \ldots (m-k+1)}{1 \cdot 2 \ldots k}.$$

We shall prove that

$$^{k+1} C_m = \frac{m (m-1) \ldots (m-k+1)(m-k)}{1 \cdot 2 \ldots k (k+1)}.$$

To obtain all combinations of m elements taken $k+1$ at a time, we shall put down all combinations of m elements k at a time and add on to each of them as the $(k+1)$th element every one of the remaining $m - k$ elements.

It is clear that in this way all combinations of m elements $k+1$ at a time will be obtained, but each will be obtained $k+1$ times.

Indeed, the combination $a_1, a_2, \ldots, a_k, a_{k+1}$ is obtained by joining the element a_1 to the combination $a_2, a_3, \ldots, a_k, a_{k+1}$, by joining the element a_2 to the combination $a_1, a_3, \ldots, a_k, a_{k+1}$ and so on, when, at last, the element a_{k+1} is joined to the combination $a_1, a_2, \ldots, a_k$.

Thus

$$^{k+1} C_m = {}^k C_m \frac{m-k}{k+1} = \frac{m (m-1) \ldots (m-k)}{1 \cdot 2 \ldots k (k+1)}.$$

Theorem 7. Whatever the numbers a and b and whatever the positive integer n the following formula holds

$$(a+b)^n = a^n + {}^1C_n a^{n-1}b + \ldots + {}^sC_n a^{n-s}b^s + \ldots + \\ + {}^{n-1}C_n \, ab^{n-1} + b^n. \tag{1}$$

(<u>Newton's Binomial Theorem</u>). For $n = 1$ we have $a + b = a + b$ and in this case the formula holds.

Let

$$(a+b)^k = a^k + {}^1C_k a^{k-1}b + {}^2C_k a^{k-2}b^2 + \ldots + b^k.$$

Then

$$(a+b)^{k+1} = (a+b)^k (a+b) = \\ = (a^k + {}^1C_k a^{k-1}b + \ldots + b^k)(a+b) = \\ = a^{k+1} + (1 + {}^1C_k)a^k b + ({}^1C_k + {}^2C_k)a^{k-1}b^2 + \ldots \\ \ldots + ({}^sC_k + {}^{s+1}C_k)a^{k-s}b^{s+1} + \ldots + b^{k+1}.$$

Taking into consideration the fact that ${}^sC_k + {}^{s+1}C_k = {}^{s+1}C_{k+1}$, which is easily proved from the expression for ${}^nC_m$, we get

$$(a+b)^{k+1} = a^{k+1} + {}^1C_{k+1}a^k b + {}^2C_{k+1}a^{k-1}b^2 + \ldots \\ \ldots + {}^{s+1}C_{k+1}a^{k-s}b^{s+1} + \ldots + b^{k+1}.$$

SOLUTIONS

<u>3</u>. Hypothesis

$$u_n = 3n - 2.$$

1) For $n = 1$ the hypothesis is correct.

2) Let

$$u_k = 3k - 2.$$

Then

$$u_{k+1} = u_k + 3 = 3k - 2 + 3 = 3(k+1) - 2.$$

<u>4</u>. Hypothesis

$$S_n = 2^n - 1.$$

1) For $n = 1$ the hypothesis is correct.

2) Let

$$S_k = 2^k - 1.$$

Then

$$S_{k+1} = S_k + 2^k = 2^{k+1} - 1.$$

<u>6</u>. 1) For $n = 1$ the proposition is correct.

2) Let

$$1^2 + 2^2 + 3^2 + \ldots + k^2 = \frac{k(k+1)(2k+1)}{6}.$$

45

Then

$$1^2 + 2^2 + 3^2 + \ldots + k^2 + (k+1)^2 =$$
$$= \frac{k(k+1)(2k+1)}{6} + (k+1)^2 = \frac{(k+1)(k+2)(2k+3)}{6}.$$

$\underline{8}$. 1) For $n = 1$ the proposition is correct.

2) Let

$$1^2 + 3^2 + 5^2 + \ldots + (2k-1)^2 = \frac{k(2k-1)(2k+1)}{3}.$$

Then

$$1^2 + 3^2 + \ldots + (2k-1)^2 + (2k+1)^2 =$$
$$= \frac{k(2k-1)(2k+1)}{3} + (2k+1)^2 = \frac{(k+1)(2k+1)(2k+3)}{3}.$$

$\underline{9}$. 1) For $n = 1$ the proposition is correct.

2) Let

$$1^3 + 2^3 + \ldots + k^3 = \left[\frac{k(k+1)}{2} \right]^2.$$

Then

$$1^3 + 2^3 + \ldots + k^3 + (k+1)^3 = \frac{k^2(k+1)^2}{4} + (k+1)^3 =$$
$$= \left[\frac{(k+1)(k+2)}{2} \right]^2.$$

$\underline{10}$. 1) For $n = 1$ the proposition is true.

2) Let

$$1 + x + x^2 + \ldots + x^k = \frac{x^{k+1} - 1}{x - 1}.$$

Then

$$1 + x + x^2 + \ldots + x^k + x^{k+1} = \frac{x^{k+1} - 1}{x - 1} + x^{k+1} = \frac{x^{k+2} - 1}{x - 1}.$$

$\underline{11}$. 1) For $n = 1$ the proposition is correct.

2) Let

$$1\cdot 2 + 2\cdot 3 + \ldots + k(k+1) = \frac{k(k+1)(k+2)}{3}.$$

Then

$$1\cdot 2 + 2\cdot 3 + \ldots + k(k+1) + (k+1)(k+2) =$$
$$= \frac{k(k+1)(k+2)}{3} + (k+1)(k+2) =$$
$$= (k+1)(k+2)\left(\frac{k}{3}+1\right) = \frac{(k+1)(k+2)(k+3)}{3}.$$

$\underline{12}$. 1) For $n=1$ the proposition is correct.

2) Let

$$1\cdot 2\cdot 3 + 2\cdot 3\cdot 4 + \ldots + k(k+1)(k+2) =$$
$$= \frac{k(k+1)(k+2)(k+3)}{4}.$$

Then

$$1\cdot 2\cdot 3 + 2\cdot 3\cdot 4 + \ldots + k(k+1)(k+2) +$$
$$+ (k+1)(k+2)(k+3) = \frac{k(k+1)(k+2)(k+3)}{4} +$$
$$+ (k+1)(k+2)(k+3) = \frac{(k+1)(k+2)(k+3)(k+4)}{4}.$$

$\underline{13}$. 1) For $n=1$ the proposition is correct.

2) Let

$$\frac{1}{1\cdot 3} + \frac{1}{3\cdot 5} + \ldots + \frac{1}{(2k-1)(2k+1)} = \frac{k}{2k+1}.$$

Then

$$\frac{1}{1\cdot 3} + \frac{1}{3\cdot 5} + \ldots + \frac{1}{(2k-1)(2k+1)} + \frac{1}{(2k+1)(2k+3)} =$$
$$= \frac{k}{2k+1} + \frac{1}{(2k+1)(2k+3)} = \frac{k+1}{2k+3}.$$

$\underline{14}$. 1) For $n=1$ the proposition is correct.

2) Let

$$\frac{1^2}{1\cdot 3} + \frac{2^2}{3\cdot 5} + \ldots + \frac{k^2}{(2k-1)(2k+1)} = \frac{k(k+1)}{2(2k+1)}.$$

Then

$$\frac{1^2}{1 \cdot 3} + \frac{2^2}{3 \cdot 5} + \ldots + \frac{k^2}{(2k-1)(2k+1)} + \frac{(k+1)^2}{(2k+1)(2k+3)} =$$
$$= \frac{k(k+1)}{2(2k+1)} + \frac{(k+1)^2}{(2k+1)(2k+3)} = (k+1)\frac{k(2k+3)+2(k+1)}{2(2k+1)(2k+3)} =$$
$$= \frac{(k+1)(2k^2+5k+2)}{2(2k+1)(2k+3)} = \frac{(k+1)(2k+1)(k+2)}{2(2k+1)(2k+3)} = \frac{(k+1)(k+2)}{2(2k+3)}.$$

<u>15</u>. 1) For $n=1$, the proposition is correct.

2) Let

$$\frac{1}{1 \cdot 4} + \frac{1}{4 \cdot 7} + \ldots + \frac{1}{(3k-2)(3k+1)} = \frac{k}{3k+1}.$$

Then

$$\frac{1}{1 \cdot 4} + \frac{1}{4 \cdot 7} + \ldots + \frac{1}{(3k-2)(3k+1)} + \frac{1}{(3k+1)(3k+4)} =$$
$$= \frac{k}{3k+1} + \frac{1}{(3k+1)(3k+4)} = \frac{k+1}{3k+4}.$$

<u>16</u>. 1) For $n=1$ the proposition is correct.

2) Let

$$\frac{1}{1 \cdot 5} + \frac{1}{5 \cdot 9} + \ldots + \frac{1}{(4k-3)(4k+1)} = \frac{k}{4k+1}.$$

Then

$$\frac{1}{1 \cdot 5} + \frac{1}{5 \cdot 9} + \ldots + \frac{1}{(4k-3)(4k+1)} + \frac{1}{(4k+1)(4k+5)} =$$
$$= \frac{k}{4k+1} + \frac{1}{(4k+1)(4k+5)} = \frac{k+1}{4k+5}.$$

<u>17</u>. 1) For $n=1$ the proposition is correct.

2) Let
$$\frac{1}{a(a+1)} + \frac{1}{(a+1)(a+2)} + \ldots + \frac{1}{(a+k-1)(a+k)} = \frac{k}{a(a+k)}.$$

Then

$$\frac{1}{a(a+1)} + \frac{1}{(a+1)(a+2)} + \ldots + \frac{1}{(a+k-1)(a+k)} +$$

$$+ \frac{1}{(a+k)(a+k+1)} = \frac{k}{a(a+k)} + \frac{1}{(a+k)(a+k+1)} = \frac{k+1}{a(a+k+1)}.$$

19. 1) For $n = 1$ and $n = 2$ the proposition is correct.

2) Let

$$u_{k-2} = \frac{\alpha^{k-1} - \beta^{k-1}}{\alpha - \beta}, \qquad u_{k-1} = \frac{\alpha^k - \beta^k}{\alpha - \beta}.$$

Then

$$u_k = (\alpha + \beta) \frac{\alpha^k - \beta^k}{\alpha - \beta} - \alpha\beta \, \frac{\alpha^{k-1} - \beta^{k-1}}{\alpha - \beta} = \frac{\alpha^{k+1} - \beta^{k+1}}{\alpha - \beta}.$$

21. 1) For $n = 0$ we have

$$\frac{1}{1+x} = \frac{1}{x-1} + \frac{2}{1-x^2}.$$

It follows that the proposition is correct.

2) Let

$$\frac{1}{1+x} + \frac{2}{1+x^2} + \frac{4}{1+x^4} + \cdots + \frac{2^k}{1+x^{2k}} = \frac{1}{x-1} + \frac{2^{k+1}}{1-x^{2k+1}}.$$

Then

$$\frac{1}{1+x} + \frac{2}{1+x^2} + \frac{4}{1+x^4} + \cdots + \frac{2^k}{1+x^{2k}} + \frac{2^{k+1}}{1+x^{2k+1}} =$$

$$= \frac{1}{x-1} + \frac{2^{k+1}}{1-x^{2k+1}} + \frac{2^{k+1}}{1+x^{2k+1}} = \frac{1}{x-1} + \frac{2^{k+2}}{1-x^{2k+2}}.$$

23. For $n = 1$ we have

$$1 - \frac{x}{1!} = - \frac{x-1}{1}.$$

For $n = 2$ we have

$$1 - \frac{x}{1!} + \frac{x(x-1)}{2!} = - \frac{x-1}{1} + \frac{x(x-1)}{2} = \frac{(x-1)(x-2)}{2!}.$$

For $n = 3$ we have

$$1 - \frac{x}{1!} + \frac{x(x-1)}{2!} - \frac{x(x-1)(x-2)}{3!} =$$

$$= \frac{(x-1)(x-2)}{2} - \frac{x(x-1)(x-2)}{6} = - \frac{(x-1)(x-2)(x-3)}{3!}.$$

This leads us to the hypothesis:

$$1 - \frac{x}{1!} + \frac{x(x-1)}{2!} - \ldots + (-1)^n \frac{x(x-1)\ldots(x-n+1)}{n!} =$$

$$= (-1)^n \frac{(x-1)(x-2)\ldots(x-n)}{n!}.$$

1) For $n = 1$ the hypothesis is correct.

2) Let

$$1 - \frac{x}{1!} + \frac{x(x-1)}{2!} - \ldots + (-1)^k \frac{x(x-1)\ldots(x-k+1)}{k!} =$$

$$= (-1)^k \frac{(x-1)(x-2)\ldots(x-k)}{k!}.$$

Then

$$1 - \frac{x}{1!} + \frac{x(x-1)}{2!} - \ldots + (-1)^k \frac{x(x-1)\ldots(x-k+1)}{k!} +$$

$$+ (-1)^{k+1} \frac{x(x-1)\ldots(x-k)}{(k+1)!} =$$

$$= (-1)^k \frac{(x-1)(x-2)\ldots(x-k)}{k!} +$$

$$+ (-1)^{k+1} \frac{x(x-1)\ldots(x-k)}{(k+1)!} =$$

$$= (-1)^{k+1} \frac{(x-1)(x-2)\ldots(x-k)}{k!} \left[\frac{x}{k+1} - 1 \right] =$$

$$= (-1)^{k+1} \frac{(x-1)(x-2)\ldots(x-k)(x-k-1)}{(k+1)!}.$$

<u>26</u>. 1) For $n = 0$ the proposition is correct.

2) Suppose that the proposition is correct for $n = k$, i.e. that

$$A_k = 11^{k+2} + 12^{2k+1}$$

is divisible by 133.

Then

$$A_{k+1} = 11^{k+3} + 12^{2(k+1)+1} = 11^{k+3} + 12^{2k+3} =$$
$$= 11 \cdot 11^{k+2} + 144 \cdot 12^{2k+1} =$$
$$= 11 \cdot 11^{k+2} + 133 \cdot 12^{2k+1} + 11 \cdot 12^{2k+1} =$$
$$= 11 \cdot (11^{k+2} + 12^{2k+1}) + 133 \cdot 12^{2k+1} =$$
$$= 11 A_k + 133 \cdot 12^{2k+1}$$

We expressed A_{k+1} as a sum of two terms, each of which is divisible by 133. This means, that A_{k+1} is divisible by 133.

<u>28</u>. For $n=1$ the proposition is correct as one straight line divides the plane into 2 parts.

Suppose k various straight lines passing through the given point divide the plane into $2k$ parts. Then the $(k+1)$th straight line passed through that point will divide two of these parts into two portions each, and thus the plane will become broken up into $2(k+1)$ parts.

<u>29</u>. 1) The straight line AB divides the plane P into two parts P_1 and P_2. If we paint P_1 white and P_2 black we shall satisfy the conditions laid down. Thus, for $n=1$ the proposition is correct.

2) Suppose the proposition to be correct for $n=k$ and the plane P to be painted in the required manner. The $(k+1)$th straight line CD divides the plane into two portions Q_1 and Q_2. In Q_1 we shall retain the colours as they are. In Q_2 we shall change white to black and black to white throughout.

Now, let O_1 and O_2 be any neighbouring areas, obtained after the drawing in of the line CD.

One of the following cases is possible:

a) O_1 and O_2 are on either side of CD.

b) O_1 and O_2 are both on the same side of CD.

In the first case O_1 and O_2 had been contained in a single portion before drawing in CD but after k lines were drawn in; they had been painted the same. Now, the one which lies in Q_1 kept its colour, but the one which lies in Q_2 changed it. That means, that in this case O_1 and O_2 are painted a different colour.

In the second case, after drawing the k lines, but before marking in CD, O_1 and O_2 were contained in two separate neighbouring areas bordering across one of the first k lines. That means that at the time O_1 and O_2 were painted differently.

If O_1 and O_2 lie in Q_1 then their colour has not changed; if they lie in Q_2 then the colour of each has changed. In either case O_1 and O_2 now differ in colour.

$\underline{34}$. 1) For $n = 1$ the proposition is correct, since

$$\frac{\sin \frac{3x}{2}}{2 \sin \frac{x}{2}} = \frac{\sin \frac{x}{2} + \left(\sin \frac{3x}{2} - \sin \frac{x}{2}\right)}{2 \sin \frac{x}{2}} = \frac{1}{2} + \cos x.$$

2) Let

$$\frac{1}{2} + \cos x + \cos 2x + \ldots + \cos kx = \frac{\sin \frac{2k+1}{2} x}{2 \sin \frac{x}{2}}.$$

Then

$$\frac{1}{2} + \cos x + \cos 2x + \ldots + \cos kx + \cos (k+1) x =$$

$$= \frac{\sin \frac{2k+1}{2} x}{2 \sin \frac{x}{2}} + \cos (k+1) x = \frac{\sin \frac{2k+1}{2} x + 2 \sin \frac{x}{2} \cos (k+1) x}{2 \sin \frac{x}{2}} =$$

$$= \frac{\sin \frac{2k+1}{2} x + \left(\sin \frac{2k+3}{2} x - \sin \frac{2k+1}{2} x\right)}{2 \sin \frac{x}{2}} = \frac{\sin \frac{2k+3}{2} x}{2 \sin \frac{x}{2}}.$$

$\underline{35}$. 1) For $n = 1$ the proposition is justified, since

$$\frac{2 \sin x - \sin 2x}{4 \sin^2 \frac{x}{2}} = \frac{2 \sin x (1 - \cos x)}{4 \sin^2 \frac{x}{2}} = \sin x.$$

2) Let
$$\sin x + 2 \sin 2x + \ldots + k \sin kx =$$
$$= \frac{(k+1) \sin kx - k \sin (k+1) x}{4 \sin^2 \frac{x}{2}}.$$

Then

$$\sin x + 2 \sin 2x + \ldots + k \sin kx + (k+1) \sin (k+1) x =$$
$$= \frac{(k+1) \sin kx - k \sin (k+1) x}{4 \sin^2 \frac{x}{2}} + (k+1) \sin (k+1) x =$$
$$= \frac{(k+1) \sin kx - k \sin (k+1) x + 2 (k+1) \sin (k+1) x (1 - \cos x)}{4 \sin^2 \frac{x}{2}} =$$
$$= \frac{(k+2) \sin (k+1) x + (k+1) \sin kx}{4 \sin^2 \frac{x}{2}} - \frac{2 (k+1) \cos x \sin (k+1) x}{4 \sin^2 \frac{x}{2}} =$$

$$= \frac{(k+2)\sin(k+1)x + (k+1)\sin kx}{4\sin \cdot \frac{x}{2}} -$$

$$- \frac{(k+1)[\sin(k+2)x + \sin kx]}{4\sin^2 \frac{x}{2}} =$$

$$= \frac{(k+2)\sin(k+1)x - (k+1)\sin(k+2)x}{4\sin^2 \frac{x}{2}}.$$

36. 1) For $n=1$ the proposition is true, since

$$\frac{2\cos x - \cos 2x - 1}{4\sin^2 \frac{x}{2}} = \frac{2\cos x - 2\cos^2 x}{4\sin^2 \frac{x}{2}} = \frac{\cos x(1 - \cos x)}{2\sin^2 \frac{x}{2}} = \cos x.$$

2) Let

$$\cos x + 2\cos 2x + \ldots + k\cos kx = \frac{(k+1)\cos kx - k\cos(k+1)x - 1}{4\sin^2 \frac{x}{2}}.$$

Then

$$\cos x + 2\cos 2x + \ldots + k\cos kx + (k+1)\cos(k+1)x =$$
$$= \frac{(k+1)\cos kx - k\cos(k+1)x - 1}{4\sin^2 \frac{x}{2}} + (k+1)\cos(k+1)x =$$

$$= \frac{(k+1)\cos kx - k\cos(k+1)x - 1}{\sin^2 \frac{x}{2}} +$$
$$+ \frac{2(k+1)\cos(k+1)x(1 - \cos x)}{4\sin^2 \frac{x}{2}} =$$

$$= \frac{(k+2)\cos(k+1)x + (k+1)\cos kx}{4\sin^2 \frac{x}{2}} -$$
$$- \frac{2(k+1)\cos x\cos(k+1)x + 1}{4\sin^2 \frac{x}{2}} =$$

$$= \frac{(k+2)\cos(k+1)x + (k+1)\cos kx}{4\sin^2 \frac{x}{2}} -$$
$$- \frac{(k+1)[\cos(k+2)x + \cos kx] + 1}{4\sin^2 \frac{x}{2}} =$$

$$= \frac{(k+2)\cos(k+1)x - (k+1)\cos(k+2)x - 1}{4\sin^2 \frac{x}{2}}.$$

$\underline{37}$. 1) For $n = 1$ the proposition is justified since

$$\frac{1}{2}\cot\frac{x}{2} - \cot x = \frac{1}{2}\cot\frac{x}{2} - \frac{1 - \tan^2\frac{x}{2}}{2\tan\frac{x}{2}} = \frac{\tan^2\frac{x}{2}}{2\tan\frac{x}{2}} = \frac{1}{2}\tan\frac{x}{2}.$$

2) Let

$$\frac{1}{2}\tan\frac{x}{2} + \frac{1}{2^2}\tan\frac{x}{2^2} + \ldots + \frac{1}{2^k}\tan\frac{x}{2^k} = \frac{1}{2^k}\cot\frac{x}{2^k} - \cot x.$$

Then

$$\frac{1}{2}\tan\frac{x}{2} + \frac{1}{2^2}\tan\frac{x}{2^2} + \ldots + \frac{1}{2^k}\tan\frac{x}{2^k} + \frac{1}{2^{k+1}}\tan\frac{x}{2^{k+1}} =$$

$$= \frac{1}{2^k}\cot\frac{x}{2^k} - \cot x + \frac{1}{2^{k+1}}\tan\frac{x}{2^{k+1}} = \frac{1}{2^{k+1}}\frac{\cot^2\frac{x}{2^{k+1}} - 1}{\cot\frac{x}{2^{k+1}}} +$$

$$+ \frac{1}{2^{k+1}\cot\frac{x}{2^{k+1}}} - \cot x = \frac{1}{2^{k+1}}\cot\frac{x}{2^{k+1}} - \cot x.$$

$\underline{38}$. 1) We have

$$\tan(\tan^{-1}2 - \tan^{-1}1) = \frac{2-1}{1+2} = \frac{1}{3}.$$

Therefore

$$\tan^{-1}2 - \tan^{-1}1 = \tan^{-1}\frac{1}{3} = \cot^{-1}3.$$

This means that for $n = 1$ the proposition is true.

2) To begin with, we shall show that

$$\cot^{-1}(2k+3) = \tan^{-1}\frac{k+2}{k+1} - \tan^{-1}1. \qquad (1)$$

Indeed

$$\tan\left(\tan^{-1}\frac{k+2}{k+1} - \tan^{-1}1\right) = \frac{\frac{k+2}{k+1} - 1}{1 + \frac{k+2}{k+1}} = \frac{1}{2k+3}.$$

This means that

$$\tan^{-1} \frac{1}{2k+3} = a \cot^{-1} (2k+3) = \tan^{-1} \frac{k+2}{k+1} - \tan^{-1} 1.$$

Suppose that the proposition is true for $n = k$, i.e.

$$\cot^{-1} 3 + \cot^{-1} 5 + \ldots + a \cot^{-1} (2k+1) =$$
$$= \tan^{-1} 2 + \tan^{-1} \frac{3}{2} + \ldots + \tan^{-1} \frac{k+1}{k} - k \tan^{-1} 1. \qquad (2)$$

We shall prove that, in that case, it is true also for $n = k+1$, i.e.

$$\cot^{-1} 3 + \cot^{-1} 5 + \ldots + \cot^{-1} (2k+3) =$$
$$= \tan^{-1} 2 + \ldots + \tan^{-1} \frac{k+2}{k+1} - (k+1) \tan^{-1} 1. \qquad (3)$$

Adding up the left-hand sides of equalities (1) and (2) and then their right-hand sides we obtain the equality (3).

$\underline{40}$. 1) For $n = 1$ the proposition is correct as

$$\sqrt{3} - i = 2 \left(\cos \frac{\pi}{6} - i \sin \frac{\pi}{6} \right).$$

2) Let

$$(\sqrt{3} - i)^k = 2^k \left(\cos \frac{k\pi}{6} - i \sin \frac{k\pi}{6} \right).$$

Then

$$(\sqrt{3} - i)^{k+1} = 2^k \left(\cos \frac{k\pi}{6} - i \sin \frac{k\pi}{6} \right) \cdot 2 \left(\cos \frac{\pi}{6} - i \sin \frac{\pi}{6} \right) =$$
$$= 2^{k+1} \left[\cos \frac{(k+1)\pi}{6} - i \sin \frac{(k+1)\pi}{6} \right].$$

$\underline{42}$. 1) For $n = 1$ the proposition is justified.

2) Let

$$(\cos x + i \sin x)^k = \cos kx + i \sin kx.$$

Then

$$(\cos x + i \sin x)^{k+1} = (\cos kx + i \sin kx)(\cos x + i \sin x) =$$
$$= \cos(k+1)x + i \sin(k+1)x.$$

$\underline{44}$. The very last phrase 'The proposition is proved' is fallacious. What is really proved is that the inequality

$$2^n > 2n + 1$$

is true for $n = k+1$, if it is true for $n = k$, where k is any natural number.

It does not necessarily follow from this that this inequality is justified at least for one value of n, and even less for any positive integer n.

In short, the mistake is this: that only Theorem 2 was proved and the Theorem 1 was not considered and no basis for induction was created. The usual way to prove Theorem 1 would be to consider $n = 1$ or $n = 2$; in both of these cases the proposition is false (but see the next problem).

$\underline{45}$. It is easy to see that 3 is the least natural value of n for which the inequality $2^n > 2n + 1$ is true.

Taking into account that the truth of the inequality for $n = k+1$ follows from its truth for $n = k$ (Problem 44) we state that the inequality is true for any natural $n \geqslant 3$.

$\underline{48}$. 1) For $n = 2$ the inequality is true for

$$1 + \frac{1}{\sqrt{2}} > \sqrt{2}.$$

2) Let

$$\frac{1}{\sqrt{1}} + \frac{1}{\sqrt{2}} + \dots + \frac{1}{\sqrt{k}} > \sqrt{k}. \tag{1}$$

We shall prove that
$$\frac{1}{\sqrt{1}} + \frac{1}{\sqrt{2}} + \dots + \frac{1}{\sqrt{k}} + \frac{1}{\sqrt{k+1}} > \sqrt{k+1}. \tag{2}$$

For any $k > 0$ the following inequality holds

$$\frac{1}{\sqrt{k+1}} > \sqrt{k+1} - \sqrt{k}. \qquad (3)$$

Indeed, the inequality (3) is obtainable from the inequality

$$1 + \sqrt{\frac{k}{k+1}} > 1$$

by multiplying both sides by $\sqrt{k+1} - \sqrt{k}$. Adding up side-wise inequalities (1) and (3) we obtain the inequality (2).

<u>49</u>. 1) For $n = 2$ the inequality takes the form of $\frac{16}{3} < 6$ and, therefore, it is correct.

2) Let

$$\frac{4^k}{k+1} < \frac{(2k)!}{(k!)^2},$$

where $k > 2$. It is easy to verify that for $k > 0$

$$\frac{4(k+1)}{k+2} < \frac{(2k+1)(2k+2)}{(k+1)^2}.$$

Therefore

$$\frac{4^k}{k+1} \cdot \frac{4(k+1)}{k+2} < \frac{(2k)!}{(k!)^2} \cdot \frac{(2k+1)(2k+2)}{(k+1)^2},$$

that is

$$\frac{4^{k+1}}{k+2} < \frac{(2k+2)!}{[(k+1)!]^2}.$$

DATE DUE

GAYLORD			PRINTED IN U.S.A.